Michaela Strachan's
REALLY
WILD
ADVENTURES

Illustrated by
Sarah Horne

W
FRANKLIN WATTS
LONDON • SYDNEY

*This book is dedicated to all the fabulous 'Really Wild' filming trips I've had over the years and, of course, to my adorable son,
Oliver Chevallier — M.S.*

First published in 2012 by Franklin Watts
Hachette Children's Books
338 Euston Road
London NW1 3BH

Franklin Watts Australia
Level 17/207 Kent Street
Sydney, NSW 2000

A CIP catalogue record for this book is available from the British Library.

ISBN 978 1 4451 1058 5 (hbk)
ISBN 978 1 4451 1340 1 (pbk)

Designer: Chris Fraser
Editors: Rachel Cooke and Melanie Palmer

Note to Teachers and Parents
Every effort has been made to ensure that the websites listed at the end of this book are
suitable for children, that they are of the highest educational value and that they contain no
inappropriate or offensive material. However, because of the nature of the Internet, it is
impossible to guarantee that the content of these sites will not be altered. We strongly
recommend that Internet access is supervised by a responsible adult.

All photos courtesy of Michaela Strachan apart from

Amander Colton/istockphoto: 23b.   Lucian Coman/Shutterstock: 15.   S.Cooper Digital/Shutterstock: 8b.
Linn Curtis/Shutterstock: 7cl.   LF File/Shutterstock: 5cl.   Glenn R. McGloughlin/Shutterstock: 23t.
Simon Nash: front cover, 18, 19tl, 19tr.   Jason Prince/istockphoto: 8c.   Ryan Richter/Shutterstock: 6cr.
robbosphoto/Shutterstock: 8t.   Pal Teravagimov/Shutterstock: 4b.
Albie Venter/Shutterstock: 14.   Gerrit de Vries/Shutterstock: 5tl.

Every attempt has been made to clear copyright. Should there be any
inadvertent omission please apply to the publisher for rectification.

Printed in China

Franklin Watts is a division of Hachette Children's Books,
an Hachette UK company. www.hachette.co.uk

Contents

A - Z of Animals

Find an animal for every letter
That was the challenge I had,
But I was in Namibia
So I guess it wasn't so bad.

Some letters were fairly easy,
Some were definitely not,
So off I went with books and binoculars
To see what I could spot.

I wanted to start with an **A**ardvark
But they're extremely hard to see,
So instead I went for an **A**ntelope
Which in Namibia was pretty easy.

The **A**ntelope was an oryx
Whose body was brown and grey.
He was large with long straight horns,
If you ask me an awesome **A**.

For **B** I found a **B**lue wildebeest,
But it's not a beast that's **b**lue,
It's dark **b**rown with a silvery sheen,
To spot it, here's a clue:

It's got curved horns like a **b**uffalo,
A **b**lack mane and tail like a horse,
A **b**eard which looks weird but this was my **B** –
A **b**eautiful **B** of course!

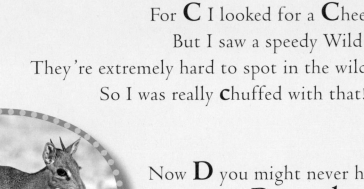

For **C** I looked for a **C**heetah,
But I saw a speedy Wild **c**at;
They're extremely hard to spot in the wild
So I was really **c**huffed with that!

Now **D** you might never have heard of:
It's the cute **D**amara **d**ik **d**ik.
It's one of the smaller antelopes –
To survive, it needs to be quick.

For **E** I went for **e**normous
African **E**lephants in a huge herd.
They were cooling off by the waterhole –
They were **e**lephantastic, if that's a word!

My **F** proved rather elusive,
A Bat-eared **F**ox is what I **f**ound.
It looks like a **f**luffy dog with huge ears
And searches for prey underground.

For **G** I went for the tallest,
It towers above the rest –
A **G**iraffe with long legs, neck and tongue,
For eating leaves from trees it's the best.

My **h**appening **H** is the **H**artebeest.
Like a cheetah, it can run really fast –
But unlike a cheetah who quickly tires,
The **H**artebeest's speed can last.

My **i**ngenious **I** is **I**mpala,
Zig zagging and leaping around,
Running at up to 90 kilometres per hour,
Jumping 3 metres in one single bound.

My **j**uicy **J** is a **J**ackal –
A scavenger that hunts as well.
You can hear them before you can see them
As they howl and they yap and they yell.

For **K** I chose something unusual –
The huge **K**ori bustard bird.
It weighs up to 18 kilos,
It's so heavy it's almost absurd!

For **L** I went for the obvious –
The **L**ion, a magnificent beast.
They're not very active till nightime,
When they hunt and enjoy a big feast.

M's for the mischievous **M**ongoose –
In a camp site we found a whole pack.
There are many different types in Namibia –
These had black stripes on their back.

For **N** we've a bird of the **n**ight,
We found the **n**octurnal **N**ightjar.
This small brown bird **n**ests in leaves
So it's hard to spot from afar.

We stayed birding to find our **O**,
But you won't see this in the sky –
It's the **O**strich which has very powerful legs
But such weedy wings it can't fly.

For **P** we had something **p**rickly –
Another creature you see in the dark –
The rather spikey but cute faced **P**orcupine,
But watch out or it'll leave its mark!

My **Q** flies in a massive flock
Which can look like a huge cloud of smoke.
It's the **Q**uelea, and they like to stick together
But to a farmer they're really no joke.

My **R** was the huge black **R**hino –
An impressive creature for sure.
Sadly they are still killed for their horns –
It's called poaching and against the law.

My **S** is for **S**potted hyena,
Whose jaws are incredibly **s**trong,
Just one bite could **s**nap off a giraffe's leg
Which we know is amazingly long.

My **T** is the **t**iny **T**ermite
And its impressive **T**ermite mound.
Sometimes it's 3 metres high
Though the nest is underground.

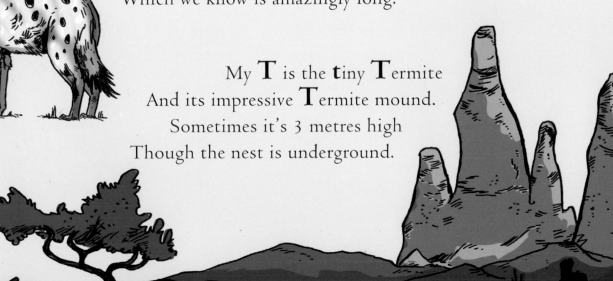

For **U** I went for some **U**ngulates,
But what are they? Well here's a clue:
They're animals with hooves, like a hippo,
Or like a zebra, or rhino too.

V is a bird you see circling
Whenever there's a carcass to eat:
They're **V**ultures, the flying scavengers
But they keep the wild tidy and neat.

W is for **w**arty **W**arthog
With its cute and charming flair –
When fleeing danger they run away fast
With their tails high up in the air!

Finding an **X** was almost impossible
But I was determined not to fail
So **X**erus inauris is what I give you,
Latin for ground squirrel with his long bushy tail.

Y is for **y**ikes, this one's tough!
But the **Y**ellow mongoose is what I chose.
They like to hang out with the ground squirrels
Sharing their underground burrows.

We've finally come to the end
And there's only one animal for **Z** –
The **Z**ebra with its black and white stripes
Like a horse in pyjamas for bed!

Lomon, the Orphaned Orangutan

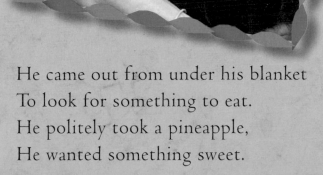

I once met an orphaned orangutan
Lomon he was called,
And when I first saw him,
His head was completely bald.

Lying under a blanket
And as thin as thin can be,
His head was all shaven,
He just laid there, limply.

At first he showed no interest
In any food at all,
Lonely, scared and shaking,
Curled up into a ball.

But after a few more days
And all the love that he was shown,
He started to recover –
How his confidence had grown!

He came out from under his blanket
To look for something to eat.
He politely took a pineapple,
He wanted something sweet.

From that first bite he didn't stop –
His tummy grew and grew.
Bananas, papaya, mango,
Anything that he could chew.

I felt a special bond with him
As the days and weeks went on –
This sweet and gentle orangutan,
My brave little Lomon.

He had to learn many lessons,
So off he went to forest school,
With lots of other orphans,
Which he thought was really cool.

Lomon soon learned how to forage
In the forest for a snack,
But as for climbing branches
He just didn't have the knack.

Whilst other orphans climbed up high
And swung between the trees,
Lomon watched from down below
His arms around his knees.

And at the end of every day,
Lomon and his forest class
Would all walk back to the centre
To meet in a gang on the grass.

One of them did somersaults,
Another found a cap,
He pulled it right down over his face
And then he took a nap.

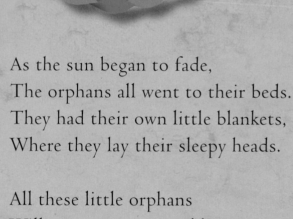

As the sun began to fade,
The orphans all went to their beds.
They had their own little blankets,
Where they lay their sleepy heads.

All these little orphans
Will grow stronger and braver in time,
One day they'll go back to the wild
But that's a few years down the line.

Next time I go back to Borneo
To meet my brave Lomon,
I am completely filled with happiness
To see how he's come on.

I see strong, red, hairy arms
Holding the branch of a tree,
Big, brown, beautiful eyes
Looking straight at me.

Lomon has learned to climb at last,
He's even building a nest.
Some nights he sleeps out in the trees;
To me he's just the best.

I can't believe how big he's grown,
He's nearly doubled his weight!
And on his head he now has hair –
He's really looking great.

He comes over to give me a cuddle,
The bond between us hasn't gone.
With a tear in my eye I give him a hug,
My gentle, adorable Lomon.

Omni and Digby

Omni and Digby were a very peculiar pair
A rhino and warthog as best friends? It's pretty rare!

Both were abandoned by their mothers in the wild
Omni just a baby, Digby as a child.

Omni's half-blind mum couldn't look after her little one,
Digby's mum was killed, he was alone and on the run.

The wardens who found them looked after them together,
Protecting them both from the hot, sunny weather.

They loved their daily trip to the muddy, muddy pool –
They liked to bathe and wallow, it kept them nice and cool.

As well as fun and frolics and lots of friendly play,
The wardens fed them milk, at least four times a day.

Omni is Digby's sidekick and a very loyal friend,
Also his hot water bottle when the day comes to an end.

Peep into Omni's night pen, it's a funny sight to see –
Digby asleep on Omni's back, all warm and snuggly.

Sometimes friendships form that are very unexpected –
A rhino and a warthog, two orphans now protected.

Never Try to Out-spit a Spitting Cobra

Never try to out-spit a spitting cobra
Coz you won't win that's for sure,
They're the most amazing spitters –
They can spit two metres or more.

I tried it once as a challenge:
'Out-spit a spitting cobra' is what it said.
What a revolting challenge, I thought,
As I frowned and scratched my head.

So we found ourselves a cobra
And a target to test it out.
My opponent was keen and feisty,
But I was full of doubt.

I stood behind the target,
Wearing goggles to be wise,
Coz when a cobra spits
It aims straight for the eyes!

His first attempt was a metre
But 2.3 was his best.
I'm sure he could've kept going,
But he slithered off, he'd lost interest.

Now it was my chance
To see how far mine would go,
I sucked on a red gob stopper
So on the target my spit would show.

My first attempt was a good one:
1.3 – now that's not bad.
For my next attempt I had to muster
All the spit that I had.

I focused on the target,
I gave the best spit that I'd got
But would it reach 2.3 metres?
Was it the perfect shot?

Oh no, it was disappointing!
Not a drop of spit could we see.
This challenge I had failed.
The cobra won with 2.3!

So never try to out-spit a spitting cobra –
In fact never try to spit at all,
Coz it really is quite revolting –
Unless you're a snake, then I guess it's cool!

The Puffin

Black and white,
Colourful beak,
Known as 'clowns of the air'.

Fun to watch,
Comical,
Full of character and flair.

What's its food?
Sand eels –
Holds 12 or more in its beak.

Stocky bird,
Penguin-like,
But its beak is unique.

Nests in burrows
On grassy slopes,
Uses the same every year.

As Winter comes,
It flies to sea –
Where it goes is not so clear.

Atlantic bound,
Away from land,
Its winter months are tough,

Bobbing around
In the sea
Which is often stormy and rough.

I love this bird.
Can you guess what it is?
It's name rhymes with … well … nuffin!

A summer visitor
To UK shores,
The wonderful, adorable PUFFIN!

The Douc Langur

Grey T-shirt,
White gloves,
Black fingers sticking out.

See if you
Can guess
What animal I'm on about?

Long arms,
Strong tail,
Swinging through the trees.

Black Shorts,
Black feet,
Red leg warmers to the knees.

Orange face,
Dark eyes,
With eyelids powder blue.

Tufty beard,
Colour white,
And here's the final clue:

Rare monkey,
Vietnam's home.
It's tricky, that's for sure –

It's the most
Colourful primate –
The red shanked DOUC LANGUR.

Elephant Orphans in Blankets

Two cute elephants playing together
Both only eight months old,
Still wearing their morning blankets
To stop them from getting cold.

Two little elephants playing
But why aren't they with their mummies,
Keeping safe with the rest of the herd,
Keeping warm under their tummies?

Well Ellie and Ollie the elephants
Got into trouble one day,
When their families were crossing a river,
They both got washed away.

The river was so fast flowing,
They both kicked with all their might,
They used their trunks as snorkels,
But they were swept right out of sight.

Weak and tired, they floated
Until they reached a bend,
Both washed up on the river bank
Thinking this could be the end.

But these two elephants were lucky,
Some rescuers spotted their plight
And took them to an orphanage
To be looked after through the night.

They woke up tired and thirsty
And were given formula milk to drink.
They were confused and frightened;
What were they both to think?

But suddenly they saw some faces
Looking into the stable door,
One, two, three baby elephants
Maybe there were more.

Their trunks came through the stable doors
To gently touch and smell.
The healing process had begun,
They started to feel well.

A few days later with blankets on
They play football in the sun.
Look! One of them's about to score –
It's a real trunkload of fun!

Later on, as the day gets warmer
And the babies start to get hot,
They go for their bathtime play in the mud
But are they clean? Hmm, I think not!

They'll have to go to elephant school
To learn how to cope in the wild,
But for now our two baby orphans
Are beginning to feel very tired.

They're taken back to their stables
And while drinking milk, their eyes close.
They fall fast asleep, safe and secure
Dreaming about what?
              …well who knows?

Why Do Penguins Make Me Smile?

What is it about penguins
That always makes me smile,
Is it the way they waddle
In that funny penguin style?

Is it their black and white outfits,
Like smart gentlemen in suits
Waddling off to a dinner dance
In awkward flipper boots?

Is it the way they bellow
With their chests puffed out all proud,
A donkey sort of honking noise
That's really rather loud?

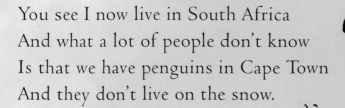

Or is it because they're birds
And yet they cannot fly?
However hard they flap their wings
They'll never reach the sky.

Well I can't decide what it is
That really amuses me,
So I decide to head off
To watch a penguin colony.

You see I now live in South Africa
And what a lot of people don't know
Is that we have penguins in Cape Town
And they don't live on the snow.

One of their homes is Boulders Beach
Where most of the time it's sunny,
People and penguins can sunbathe together,
Well I guess that's pretty funny.

I sit and watch a penguin
Doing his morning preen.
Using his beak to wash himself
To keep him oiled and clean.

He takes so long to preen himself
Do you know the reason why?
It waterproofs his feathers
And helps him to stay dry.

Penguins look very funny
When they waddle across the beach
Stopping to scratch that itch
That's almost out of reach.

Waddle, waddle, stop and preen
Am I looking nice and clean?

It's amazing to see how penguins
Climb up and down on the rocks,
Hopping, slipping, sliding, falling
Always getting knocks.

Up they hop,
Down they slide.
They're out of control
As they all collide!

21

I watch a penguin digging
Making himself a comfy nest –
A burrow in the sand
In the spot he thinks is best.

He flicks and kicks and kicks and flicks –
The sand flies everywhere,
Right into the face of his neighbour
But his neighbour doesn't seem to care.

I decide to put my goggles on
And I dive into the sea,
Where I can see these little penguins
Swim so perfectly.

They dive deep down to get their food,
They swim at a really fast pace.
They swim and glide and glide and swim
With elegance and grace.

So I decide that the African penguin
Is full of humour and charm
And it's in need of our protection
To keep it out of harm.

These penguin numbers have dropped
At an incredibly alarming rate
So if we want to save them
We must act before it's too late.

We need to protect and respect
These adorable little birds.
Why do they make us smile?
Well it's hard to put down in words . . .

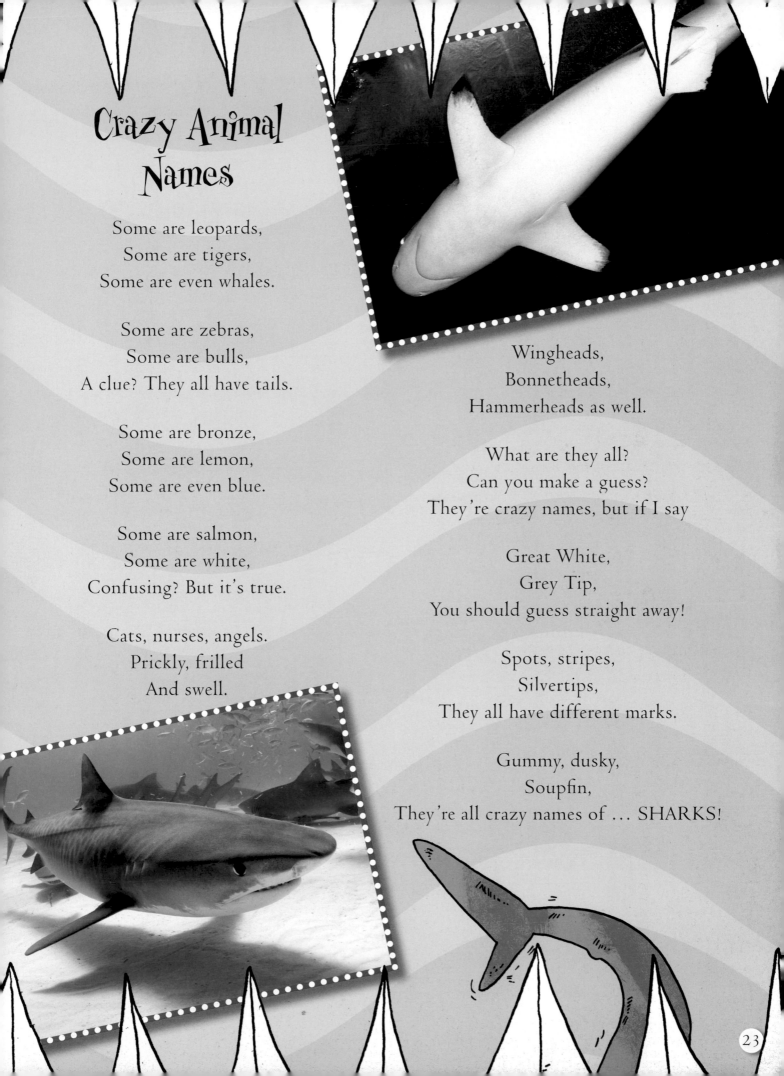

Crazy Animal Names

Some are leopards,
Some are tigers,
Some are even whales.

Some are zebras,
Some are bulls,
A clue? They all have tails.

Some are bronze,
Some are lemon,
Some are even blue.

Some are salmon,
Some are white,
Confusing? But it's true.

Cats, nurses, angels.
Prickly, frilled
And swell.

Wingheads,
Bonnetheads,
Hammerheads as well.

What are they all?
Can you make a guess?
They're crazy names, but if I say

Great White,
Grey Tip,
You should guess straight away!

Spots, stripes,
Silvertips,
They all have different marks.

Gummy, dusky,
Soupfin,
They're all crazy names of ... SHARKS!

Polar Bear Dentistry

Crazy animal challenges,
Oh yes I've had a few,
From stealing a kiss off a hummingbird
To getting knee deep in bat poo!

But one of my scariest challenges
Was to pull a tooth from a polar bear.
I've never heard of a polar bear dentist,
Do they sit in a polar bear chair?

"Now don't be silly," they said,
As we flew North to the cold and the snow,
Coz polar bears are found in the Arctic
And not the Antarctic you know.

So how do you do this tooth pulling?
Well don't try while the bear's awake!
Polar bears can hunt humans
So my life would've been at stake.

So off we flew in a helicopter
To search for a polar bear.
Once found, we had to dart it
Which is tricky from up in the air.

We waited for the bear to sleep
Before we all got going.
My challenge: to extract the tooth
Without the poor bear knowing.

The scientists had to take some blood
And a sample of skin from his ear,
It's used for polar bear research.
They also marked the bear's rear.

Then it was my turn
To play my dentist part,
I got head to head with this great
   white bear
So I could make a start.

We used a huge pair of pliers
To make the tooth come out,
It really wasn't easy —
But the challenge is what it's about.

We then ran back to safety,
Holding the precious polar bear tooth.
But why did we need to extract it?
Too many sweets? No, here's the truth:

The tooth tells us the age of the bear,
They also test the blood and skin.
They look for signs of pollution
And check the bear's not too thin.

Polar bears are such fabulous creatures,
On snow they're exciting to see,
But to get head to head whilst pulling a tooth
Is one crazy challenge, I'm sure you'll agree.

Wrapped Up Bats

I went on a trip to Australia
To film for *The Really Wild Show*.
We filmed kangaroos and koalas,
Lots of animals that you'll know.

But I'm not going to tell you
About all of that,
My story is about
A little fruit bat.

They're spectacled flying foxes
But please don't be appalled,
They're not foxes wearing glasses,
It's just what they are called.

They like to live in forests
But some of them get sick,
They get poisoned by the bite
Of a tiny, tiny tick.

When a bat gets poisoned by the tick
Its legs can grip no more,
They get what's called paralysis
And fall down to the floor.

Unable to move, these bats
Would surely have a sorry end
But a team has come to save them
Until they're on the mend.

Some of the mums have babies
Still clinging to their chest,
They're taken away from Mum
So she can recover and rest.

The babies are adorable
  Their foxy faces look so sweet,
  They all have to be hand fed
  With a bottle and a teat.

They're wrapped in colourful blankets
All stripy, spotty or pink.
The teats all ready in their mouths,
They're thirsty and want to drink.

They twitch their little noses
As they suck the bottle dry.
All snuggled in their blankets,
Let's hope they don't all cry.

Sometimes they lose their voices
Because they cry so much,
Wanting to know where their mums are –
They miss their mother's touch.

But soon the mummies get better,
Mummy and baby can reunite.
Their legs no longer paralysed,
  Wings strong enough for flight.

So next time you think bats are scary
And only come out at Halloween,
Think of the cute wrapped up babies
And then you'll smile instead of scream!

Animal Pop Idols

I once went on a mission to look for an animal star.
Pop Idol with a difference, it was really quite bizarre!

Birds, mammals and insects were the first to come along.
Each one ready to compete and sing their favourite song.

The sea lions came in force, but their smell just put me off,
Their song was very noisy, more like a barking cough.

The seagulls flew down in a flock and sounded all the same;
If they were a boy band, Gulls Aloud could be their name!

The camels sounded awful and had too much attitude,
I told them but they got the hump and said that I was rude!

The lions roared a mighty roar, they were the loudest band
But when they tried to eat the judge it all got out of hand.

The hyenas had a raucous laugh which really made me giggle.
The bees buzzed through their little tune with a honey-finding wiggle.

Then came a last minute entry, a real pop idol treasure,
Hear its song and you'll agree it's a treat and a pleasure.

It was the humpback whale with a waterproof microphone.
His song was just beautiful and had such a perfect tone.

The tune was very different with a wonderful haunting sound.
Of all the contestants that I saw he was the best I'd found.

So the animal pop idol crown I now can award
To the humpback whale, whose song we all applaud.

More about the Animals

A to Z of Animals (page 4)

I was really given this challenge — in the Etosha National Park, Namibia, filming for Channel 5's *Michaela's Wild Challenges*. We did it in two days. It was hard but a lot of fun. I have changed some of the animals for the sake of the poem. A to Zs are always fun to do although some letters are really tricky. Try it with birds, e.g. A for albatross, B for blue tit, C for crow, D for dipper, E for eagle, etc!! See what you can come up with (you can always cheat for X and do an eXtraordinary sparrow)!

Lomon, the Orphaned Orangutan (page 9)

Lomon was one of many orphans we filmed for the BBC series *Orangutan Diary*. We filmed the series at the Borneo Orangutan Survival Foundation's Nyaru Menteng Rescue Sanctuary. The sanctuary rescues, rehabilitates and eventually releases orangutans back into the wild. Wild organgutans face many threats: hunting, illegal trading, forest fires, illegal logging, but the biggest is the clearing of their forest homes for the palm oil industry. Palm oil is used in many everyday products from shampoo to crisps. Many charities work hard to save orangutans. If you'd like to find out more check out the website: www.orangutanprotectionfoundation.org.

Omni and Digby (page 12)

We filmed Omni and Digby at Lewa Wildlife Conservancy in Kenya for *The Really Wild Show*. They were a cute but unlikely pair.

It's unusual for different animal species to bond but it does sometimes happen, especially if the animals are orphans and brought up together or if they're in captivity. Here are some other odd relationships: Moses the crow and Cassie the kitten, Owen the baby hippo and Mzee the giant tortoise, Aochan the rat snake and Gohan the hamster (Gohan is Japanese for meal!). The oddest relationship, I've heard of has to be the wild leopard in India who befriended a domestic cow and used to visit it at night for a snuggle and a clean!

Never Try to Out-spit a Spitting Cobra (page 14)

This is based on a challenge we filmed for the Channel 5 series *Michaela's Wild Challenge* in South Africa. Our star snake was a Mozambique spitting cobra about 1.2m in length. Cobras lift their heads up high when they're threatened and flare out the 'hood' around their necks which looks pretty ferocious. The spit is actually venom which they squirt from their fangs. Although it's harmless if your skin is intact, it is extremely painful if the spit hits your eyes and it can cause blindness, so I wore goggles! The spit is used mainly for defence. The snake kills its prey — rodents, birds, lizards, toads and other snakes — with a venomous bite.

The Puffin (page 16)

Puffins are extraordinary birds and Atlantic puffins are one of my favourites. They spend most of their lives at sea. Each spring they come to land-based breeding colonies on the North Atlantic seacoasts and islands.

They choose a partner for life and couples often return to the same burrow site year after year! Baby puffins are called pufflings. Puffin numbers are being badly affected by a decline in their main food source, sand eels.

The Douc Langur (page 17)

The red shanked douc langur has to be one of the most stunning monkeys in the world. They live in the forest treetops of Vietnam and Laos. Their main diet is leaves but they also eat fruit, flowers and shoots. This gives them huge stomachs which make them look like pot bellied men and they tend to burp a lot! They are endangered mainly due to habitat loss and hunting. These beautiful animals are hunted for the pet trade, food and Chinese medicine.

Elephant Orphans in Blankets (page 18)

This poem is based on true stories of orphaned elephants rescued by the David Sheldrick Wildlife Trust in Kenya. We filmed their work for a BBC series called *Elephant Diaries*. Although I have made up the orphans' names, the poem is a typical story: elephant calves really do get into trouble crossing rivers with their herds and, once at the Trust, the orphans really do wear blankets, drink milk from huge bottles and sleep in stables. The orphans I saw in the nursery in Nairobi really are quite good at football, too! If you'd like to help the elephants in the orphanage, check out their website: www.sheldrickwildlifetrust.org.

Why Do Penguins Make Me Smile? (page 20)

A lot of people don't realise penguins live in a warm country, but they do. The African penguin is found on the south-west coast of Africa, far from the snow and ice where most penguins live. Sadly though, the number of these penguins is dropping dramatically for many reasons: pollution, oil spills, over fishing, climate change, loss of habitat and living too close to humans. One of the organisations that helps African penguins is SANCCOB, the South African Foundation for the Conservation of Coastal Birds. If you'd like to help the penguins and find out more about them, check out the SANCCOB website: www.sanccob.co.za.

Crazy Animal Names (page 23)

I'm a big fan of sharks and have swum with many, from hammerheads to whale sharks, great whites to lemons. Sharks have had such a bad press but in fact they only kill around 5 people a year. People, however, kill around 100 million sharks every year! Here are some crazy facts: more people get bitten by other people in New York every year than get bitten by sharks all over the world. More people are killed from falling coconuts than from sharks. And you are more likely to die falling out of bed than die from a shark attack! So no more scary sharks but lots of scary New Yorkers, coconuts and deadly beds!

Polar Bear Dentistry (page 24)

This was an awesome challenge for Channel 5's *Michaela's Wild Challenge*. It was amazing to see a polar bear close up. However, polar bear numbers are dropping and one of the main reasons is climate change. Basically, their environment is melting. Polar bears hunt on ice, mainly seals. Every year the sea freezes

over, but this annual freeze is starting later and lasting less time, so the bears have less time to hunt on solid ice. The result is a lot of hungry bears. That's why all the research done on bears is so important.

Wrapped Up Bats (page 26)

Spectacled flying foxes are handsome bats. They live in rainforests and roost in huge groups high up in the trees. The roosts are known as camps and, in the daytime, they tend to be really noisy with thousands of chattering bats! They fly out to feed at night and they eat flowers as well as fruit. They get their name from the light coloured fur around their eyes which makes them look like they are wearing spectacles! The ticks described in the poem are a real threat to these bats. If you'd like to find out more check out the Tolga Bat Hospital website: www.tolgabathospital.org.

Animal Pop Idol (page 28)

We actually did this as a piece for the BBC's *The Really Wild Show* when we were filming in San Francisco, although I have changed some of the animals for this poem. I chose my winner as the humpback whale because its song is quite extraordinary and hauntingly beautiful. It's a very long and complex tune made by the male and lasts up to half an hour, travelling huge distances through the water. It's made up of eerie moans, groans, squeals and whistles. No one really knows why they sing, maybe it's to attract a female, maybe it's to communicate to other males or maybe they really are just trying to be the latest pop idols!

Index of First Lines